TAKE THE LEAD

ALTO SAXOPHONE

Musicals

Series Editor: Anna Joyce

Editorial, production and recording: Artemis Music Limited • Design and production: Space DPS Limited • Published 2001

IMP

International MUSIC Publications

Demonstration

Backing

Fame
from *Fame*

Words by Dean Pitchford
Music by Michael Gore

Bright pop feel

Demonstration

Backing

Food Glorious Food

from *Oliver*

Words and Music by Lionel Bart

© 1963 & 2001 Lakeview Music Publishing Co Ltd, London SW10 0SZ

If I Were A Rich Man
from *Fiddler On The Roof*

Words by Sheldon Harnick
Music by Jerry Bock

Demonstration   Backing

Demonstration   Backing

Over The Rainbow
from *The Wizard Of Oz*

Words by E Y Harburg
Music by Harold Arlen

Ballad tempo

Demonstration   Backing

Send In The Clowns
from *A Little Night Music*

Words and Music by
Stephen Sondheim

Slowly

Demonstration

Backing

Singin' In The Rain
from *Singin' In The Rain*

Words by Arthur Freed
Music by Nacio Herb Brown

Tomorrow
from *Annie*

Words by Martin Charnin
Music by Charles Strouse

Demonstration

Backing

Wouldn't It Be Loverly
from *My Fair Lady*

Words by Alan Jay Lerner
Music by Frederick Loewe

19

Printed by Halstan & Co. Ltd., Amersham, Bucks., England